FLOWER·FAIRIES
OF·THE·WINTER

Designed by Malcolm Smythe

Colour retouched by Elsa Godfrey

Copyright © 1985 The Estate of Cicely Mary Barker

This edition first published in hardback 1985,
and in paperback 1987 by
Blackie and Son Limited
7 Leicester Place, London WC2H 7BP

Reprinted 1988 (both editions)

British Library Cataloguing in Publication Data
Barker, Cicely Mary
    Flower fairies of the winter.——(The flower fairies)
    I. Title   II. Series
    821'.912   PR6003.A6786
    ISBN 0-216-91687-9
    ISBN 0-216-92151-1 Pbk

Printed in Great Britain by Cambus Litho, East Kilbride

FLOWER·FAIRIES OF·THE·WINTER

With a biography of the author

Poems and pictures by
CICELY MARY BARKER

BLACKIE

THE SONG OF THE
SNOWDROP FAIRY

Deep sleeps the Winter,
 Cold, wet, and grey;
Surely all the world is dead;
 Spring is far away.
Wait! the world shall waken;
 It is not dead, for lo,
The Fair Maids of February
 Stand in the snow!

SNOWDROP

SONG OF THE
~~YEW~~ FAIRY

Here, on the dark and solemn Yew,
   A marvel may be seen,
Where waxen berries, pink and new,
   Appear amid the green.

I sit a-dreaming in the tree,
   So old and yet so new;
One hundred years, or two, or three
   Are little to the Yew.

I think of bygone centuries,
   And seem to see anew
The archers face their enemies
   With bended bows of Yew.

YEW

THE SONG OF THE
WINTER JASMINE FAIRY

All through the Summer my leaves were green,
But never a flower of mine was seen;
Now Summer is gone, that was so gay,
And my little green leaves are shed away.
       In the grey of the year
       What cheer, what cheer?

The Winter is come, the cold winds blow;
I shall feel the frost and the drifting snow;
But the sun can shine in December too,
And this is the time of my gift to you.
       See here, see here,
       My flowers appear!

The swallows have flown beyond the sea,
But friendly Robin, he stays with me;
And little Tom-Tit, so busy and small,
Hops where the jasmine is thick on the wall;
       And we say: "Good cheer!
       We're here! We're here!"

WINTER JASMINE

THE SONG OF THE
RUSH-GRASS AND COTTON-GRASS
FAIRIES

Safe across the moorland
 Travellers may go,
If they heed our warning –
 We're the ones who know!

Let the footpath guide you –
 You'll be safely led;
There is bog beside you
 Where you cannot tread!

Mind where you are going!
 If you turn aside
Where you see us growing,
 Trouble will betide.

Keep you to the path, then!
 Hark to what we say!
Else, into the quagmire
 You will surely stray.

RUSH-GRASS & COTTON-GRASS

THE SONG OF THE
SPINDLE BERRY FAIRY

See the rosy-berried Spindle
All to sunset colours turning,
Till the thicket seems to kindle,
Just as though the trees were burning.
While my berries split and show
Orange-coloured seeds aglow,
One by one my leaves must fall:
Soon the wind will take them all.
Soon must fairies shut their eyes
For the Winter's hushabies;
But, before the Autumn goes,
Spindle turns to flame and rose!

SPINDLE BERRY

THE SONG OF THE
LORDS AND LADIES FAIRY

Fairies, when you lose your way,
    From the dance returning,
In the darkest undergrowth
    See my candles burning!
These shall make the pathway plain
Homeward to your beds again.

LORDS AND LADIES

THE SONG OF THE
PLANE TREE FAIRY

You will not find him in the wood,
    Nor in the country lane;
But in the city's parks and streets
    You'll see the Plane.

O turn your eyes from pavements grey,
    And look you up instead,
To where the Plane tree's pretty balls
    Hang overhead!

When he has shed his golden leaves,
    His balls will yet remain,
To deck the tree until the Spring
    Comes back again!

PLANE TREE

THE SONG OF THE
BURDOCK FAIRY

Wee little hooks on each brown little bur,
(Mind where you're going, O Madam and Sir!)
How they will cling to your skirt-hem and stocking!
Hear how the Burdock is laughing and mocking:
Try to get rid of me, try as you will,
Shake me and scold me, I'll stick to you still,
  I'll stick to you still!

BURDOCK

THE SONG OF THE
PINE TREE FAIRY

A tall, tall tree is the Pine tree,
    With its trunk of bright red-brown –
The red of the merry squirrels
    Who go scampering up and down.

There are cones on the tall, tall Pine tree,
    With its needles sharp and green;
Small seeds in the cones are hidden,
    And they ripen there unseen.

The elves play games with the squirrels
    At the top of the tall, tall tree,
Throwing cones for the squirrels to nibble –
    I wish I were there to see!

PINE TREE

THE SONG OF THE
HOLLY FAIRY

O, I am green in Winter-time,
  When other trees are brown;
Of all the trees (So saith the rhyme)
  The holly bears the crown.
December days are drawing near
  When I shall come to town,
And carol-boys go singing clear
Of all the trees (O hush and hear!)
  The holly bears the crown!

For who so well-beloved and merry
As the scarlet Holly Berry?

HOLLY

THE SONG OF THE
BOX TREE FAIRY

Have you seen the Box unclipped,
Never shaped and never snipped?
Often it's a garden hedge,
Just a narrow little edge;
Or in funny shapes it's cut,
And it's very pretty; *but* –

But, unclipped, it is a tree,
Growing as it likes to be;
And it has its blossoms too;
Tiny buds, the Winter through,
Wait to open in the Spring
In a scented yellow ring.

And among its leaves there play
Little blue-tits, brisk and gay.

BOX TREE

THE SONG OF THE
OLD-MAN'S-BEARD FAIRY

This is where the little elves
Cuddle down to hide themselves;
Into fluffy beds they creep,
Say good-night, and go to sleep.

OLD-MAN'S-BEARD

THE SONG OF THE
BLACKTHORN FAIRY

The wind is cold, the Spring seems long
    a-waking;
    The woods are brown and bare;
Yet this is March: soon April will be making
    All things most sweet and fair.

See, even now, in hedge and thicket tangled,
    One brave and cheering sight:
The leafless branches of the Blackthorn,
     spangled
    With starry blossoms white!

BLACKTHORN

THE SONG OF THE
TOTTER-GRASS FAIRY

The leaves on the tree-tops
   Dance in the breeze;
Totter-grass dances
   And sways like the trees –

Shaking and quaking!
   While through it there goes,
Dancing, a Fairy,
   On lightest of toes.

TOTTER-GRASS

THE SONG OF THE
WINTER ACONITE FAIRY

Deep in the earth
I woke, I stirred.
I said: "Was that the Spring I heard?
For something called!"
"No, no," they said;
"Go back to sleep. Go back to bed.

"You're far too soon;
The world's too cold
For you, so small." So I was told.
But how could I
Go back to sleep?
I could not wait; I had to peep!

Up, up I climbed,
And here am I.
How wide the earth! How great the sky!
O wintry world,
See me awake!
Spring calls, and comes; 'tis no mistake.

WINTER ACONITE

THE SONG OF THE
CHRISTMAS TREE FAIRY

The little Christmas Tree was born
    And dwelt in open air;
It did not guess how bright a dress
    Some day its boughs would wear;
Brown cones were all, it thought, a tall
    And grown-up Fir would bear.

O little Fir! Your forest home
    Is far and far away;
And here indoors these boughs of yours
    With coloured balls are gay,
With candle-light, and tinsel bright,
    For this is Christmas Day!

A dolly-fairy stands on top,
    Till children sleep; then she
(A live one now!) from bough to bough
    Goes gliding silently.
O magic sight, this joyous night!
    O laden, sparkling tree!

CHRISTMAS TREE

—•*About the author*•—

CICELY MARY BARKER was born in Croydon on 28th June 1895. She suffered from epilepsy as a child, and because of her frail health her parents chose to educate her at home, with the help of a governess. Although delicate, she was vivacious and pretty, and had a happy childhood in a secure family background. Her life as a whole could best be described as uneventful, and her character serene.

Her family home, where she spent most of her life, was at 23, The Waldrons, South Croydon. Her father, Walter, was a seed merchant in the City of London who died young, possibly from an illness contracted in the course of his work.

Her mother, Mary Oswald, came from an old Croydon family who lived for many years in the Old Palace in central Croydon, a mediaeval building which, until the end of the eighteenth century, belonged to the Archbishops of Canterbury, six of whom are buried in the nearby parish church of St. John the Baptist.

Cicely Barker's eldest sister, Dorothy, was devoted to both Cicely and her mother and took the major share of responsibility for organising their household. She did the cooking and shopping as well as running a small kindergarten school in their house.

Cicely began to draw when she was very young, although she had no formal artistic training. As a young woman she joined the Croydon Art Society, of which she was a lifelong member. The artists she met at the Society must have given her much useful advice and guidance, and helped her to develop her natural talent.

She rarely travelled far from her home, and usually spent her summer holidays on the South coast at Bognor or Deal, in the company of her mother and sister Dorothy. There she spent her time sketching children at play on the beach or walking on the Downs in search of landscapes to paint. She also went on a number of working holidays with a fellow artist and friend, Margaret Tarrant, well-known for her religious paintings, in which nature is shown in harmony with and as a background to figures of Christ, or angels, often surrounded by children. The two artists had much in common and probably influenced each other's work.

Children were always Miss Barker's favourite subjects, and among her earliest works were two sets of postcards: *Children of the Allies*, issued during or shortly after the First World War, and *Shakespeare's Children*, portraits of the youngest characters in Shakespeare's plays, such as Falstaff's page, Titania's changeling. Later came a set of seaside postcards with idyllic beach scenes – children paddling, making sand pies and sand castles, or looking at the sea through a telescope. All three series of cards were published by the firm of J. Salmon in Sevenoaks, Kent.

Cicely Barker was a deeply religious person and some of her best and most memorable work had a religious theme. This included a set of devotional postcards for an American company, many Christmas cards for charities and missions, *The Children's Book of Hymns* for Blackie, and *He Leadeth Me*, a collection of bible stories written by her sister, Dorothy, (also published by Blackie).

There are examples of her work in a number of churches in the area around her home; for example in St. George's Waddon she painted a mural illustrating the parable of the great supper (Luke 14, verses 16-24), and for the memorial chapel in the Methodist Church, Norbury, she was commissioned to paint a large panel (7 ft by 4 ft, oils on wood) entitled "Out of Great Tribulation". The picture is dated 1948 and the theme is Christ bringing comfort to those who have suffered in war. As in so much of her work, it is children who take the centre of the stage, standing on either side of Christ.

Although the building for which this painting was commissioned has now been demolished, the painting is still in the possession of the Methodist Church.

Cicely Barker's local church, which she attended regularly, usually sitting quietly at the back, was St. Andrew's, Croydon. There she decorated the font with paintings of the seven sacraments, using regular churchgoers as models. Her other gifts to this church are two beautifully illustrated baptismal rolls, hanging on the wall close to the font.

Her aunt Alice, who was her mother's eldest sister, had the rare distinction of being a Head Deaconess in the Church of England. Her ministry was mainly at Llandaff, South Wales, and Cicely painted a triptych for the Diocesan House there, illustrating the feeding of the five thousand.

Cicely Barker is believed, also, to have drawn up a number of designs for stained glass windows. Critics have detected in her religious paintings and illustrations the influence of the nineteenth century artists of the Pre-Raphaelite Brotherhood. Like theirs, her style was often one of heightened realism, and in her oil paintings she used clear, luminous colours. Though the subjects of her paintings were mystical, the figures she portrayed were nonetheless clearly "ordinary" people. She was, herself, aware of Pre-Raphaelite influence, and in an interview she gave in 1964 said that she was very interested in the pre-Raphaelites, and particularly admired Millais and Burne-Jones. She had made a special journey to Birmingham to see an exhibition of their paintings.

The first Flower Fairy Book, *Flower Fairies of the*

Spring, was published by Blackie in 1923. With the encouragement of Mr. Walter Blackie, grandson of the founder of the firm, new titles were gradually added to the series, the seventh and last, *Flower Fairies of the Wayside*, being published in 1948. Since their first publication the Flower Fairies have been firm favourites with both adults and children. Many parents buying the books now for their children realise as they look at them once again that they learned almost all they know about botany from Cicely Barker's illustrations, which accurately portray not just the appearance of the flowers, but also their essential character and 'spirit'. Many, perhaps most, of the poems in these books were written by her sister.

Part of the charm of the Flower Fairy illustrations is the fact that the fairies themselves are all individuals and look like real children. This is because the pictures are, in a way, portraits. Many of the models were children who attended the kindergarten run by Miss Barker's sister, Dorothy. Others were 'faces in a crowd' – people she met in the street or elsewhere and invited back to her studio to sit for her, because she found their faces particularly attractive or striking. The studio was a wooden building in the back garden of the Barkers' house, next to a large hen-run.

Although best-known for the Flower Fairies, Miss Barker also illustrated two popular collections of nursery rhymes and was author of a fairy story, *Groundsel and Necklaces* (later re-titled *The Fairy's Gift*) and the near-classic story of a young girl fostered by swans, *The Lord of the Rushie River*. This was inspired by a dream she had as a child, of flying on a swan's back.

The illustrations are particularly fine, some reminiscent of paintings of Leda and the Swan. Blackie also commissioned her to illustrate the covers of a series of story books and to contribute to a number of compilations of story and rhyme such as *Our Darling's First Book*. These illustrations reflect a nostalgic image of childhood, full of innocence and security.

She always enjoyed her working relationship with her publishers, Blackie, and thought of them as her friends. Money was never of much concern to her, and she was grateful for the steady income from her books.

Towards the end of her life, Cicely Barker inherited a small house in the country, near Storrington in Sussex where she lived for a short time, but she felt isolated there and found the traffic on the narrow lanes rather daunting for an elderly pedestrian. So she moved into Storrington itself to live near friends. She died in Worthing in February 1973, shortly before the fiftieth anniversary of the first of her much-loved Flower Fairy books, which have proved a lasting memorial and have rarely been out of print since their first publication.